Tales from the Tin Tabernacle

by

George Andrew

DARF PUBLISHERS LIMITED
London
1989

FIRST PUBLISHED 1989

Cartoons drawn by: Ray Griffiths

ISBN 1 85077 207 X

Printed in Great Britain by A. Wheaton & Co Ltd, Exeter

Contents

Foreword

Chaucerian in origin, owing perhaps more to Tom Sharpe's Wilt than The Widow of Bath, here are characters drawn from . . . and easily recognised by . . . weekend cricketers throughout the country.

During the course of this romp through the playing fields of England's villages, we encounter and share the problems presented to Geoff, the team captain, including his discovery of penicillin, several decades too late.

Strategy plays an important part in the success of the team, until it is pre-empted by opposing captains.

Horatio, a thirteen and a half stone Irish Wolfhound contributes to a notable defeat.

Elvis, the fast bowler, combining the effects of the two main influences on his life, Fred Trueman and Emmanuelle, succumbs to a magic potion concocted by the village elders and alters the course of history.

The entrepreneurial groundsman combines an advertising campaign with supplying the team with lamb chops and cropping the grass with sheep.

Piers ffrenche-epistle joins the team and stars in the game against The University.

Winston's feet are encased in carpet slippers to stop him stamping on the pitch and cracking it from corner to corner.

We discover the ten 'real' ways of being out with the help of Nigel, the opening bat and are given a lesson in umpiring by Ben, the elder twin. The delights of touring are revealed together with the season's special awards.

"The Tin Tabernacle"

CHAPTER ONE

Ben, the Elder Twin's Story

In which we are granted an insight into the Tin Tabernacle and receive a lesson in umpiring.

One sure method identifying whether one is in the land of real cricket is to look at the scoreboard. If there are only two nails at the top you are there. No side has ever scored a hundred on this ground.

The hall mark of a village cricket side has always been the Tin Tabernacle. This is built, or rather home-made in the best possible sense, of materials which ensure its place in the list of Gothic Horrors of the century. The foundation of concrete made from the remnants of bags of cement of archaeological significance is the base from which the Doric Pillars of woodworm infested holly stakes rise ... to these the sides and roof are fixed with a variety of nails, screws, wire, string and hope. Colour is an important factor. From the trains which pass at irregular intervals along the track (which is always situated behind the bowler's arm), the passengers are granted brief glimpses of the red ... orange ... yellow ... green ... blue ... indigo and vermillion as it reflects off the sheen of the ever-wet roof. Those of you who for years have struggled to remember the mnemonic ... RICHARD OF YORK GAVE BATTLE IN VAIN ... in order to get the sequence of the spectrum right, now have an alternative. How about ... RATHER OLD YUCKY GALVANISED BATTERED IRON VERANDAH. Except that it isn't ... a verandah ... since it is situated well to the leeward of the pavilion where it fights a losing battle against well-fertilized foilage. Forerunner of the Superloo, destined to outlast all modern counterparts. The between-innings competition . . . "Who can drown the most spiders?" . . . is fraught with dangers. Infiltrating between the corroded, corrugated walls, waving hungrily in the breeze, fronds of nettles wait to catch the unwary. Venus traps waiting for the flies to open . . . giving rise to screams of anguish and the heartfelt cry of . . . "Take away the pain, but leave the swelling."

Did you really think that the long spikes attached to cricket boots were put there in order to let fast bowlers rip up lovingly tended pitches? Well, rolled once and cut on Saturday morning. No. They are to counteract the eye-closing, nose-twitching cocktail, (and there's another derivation), containing three parts Jeyes and one part tar . . . at the beginning of the day anyway . . . which swirls uneasily over the crumbling concrete floor. In the days of canvas boots it became essential that the lethal mixture didn't soak through to the socks . . . however unsavoury *they* might be . . . so . . . as ever with cricket . . . soles were raised, literally.

Let us venture inside to meet two of the stalwarts of the team. The game is over . . . the last lap in the Saturday ritual before the pub opens is being completed. Bill and Ben . . . inseparable twins on whom the club had been refounded after the war . . . stand side by side . . . right hands cupped 'over' protectively as they spray the insects.

"Good win," Bill is strong on philosophy.

"Mmmm, I'm glad we saved that one for today." Ben chuckled. "Shall I tell them why and how later?"

"Let them chew on it for a bit. Then if they get stroppy you could have a quiet word."

Guile plays a large part in the strategies of real village cricket. Matches are remembered for the method by which victory was achieved.

Take the game in question.

Batting second on a cow-pat affected pitch, the village were in trouble. The opposition's fast bowler had ripped through the cream

"Bill and Ben"

of the batting, leaving Ben to face the last five balls of the match, with the scores tied and only his wicket to fall.

But Ben was a veritable font of knowledge on the laws of the game . . . as was Bill, who was the umpire at the bowler's end.

Final adjustments were made to the field placings, an extra slip was added to the cordon of three and the bowler commenced his run.

Ben's stance as a batsman had caused greater controversy in the Fox than that of Peter Willey. Ben stood very straight, feet together facing directly at the stumps at the other end, his bat held in front of him. Like Willey his feet would move just as the bowler reached his delivery point . . . a shuffle back towards the leg side.

The second ball of the over was delivered . . . Ben shuffled . . . his middle stump cartwheeled towards the wicket keeper. The fielding side erupted in a frenzy of leaping, back-slapping and unrestrained rejoicing.

"No ball!" the umpire's voice was loud and clear. He gathered the stumps and bails and walked to the pavilion.

Later, in the public bar of the Fox, Ben explained to his captive audience. "I knew I'd got no chance," he said, "so as the bowler ran up I shuffled the other way . . . not towards the leg side but backwards on to the slips."

"So what?" The opposition were none too pleased, either at the result or being made to wait for an explanation.

"Well, you realise that that would place five fielders behind me on the leg-side. That is against the laws and Bill had no choice . . . he had to call a no-ball."

"Horatio"

CHAPTER TWO

Geoff, the Captain's Story

In which the captain gains the substance which will form the basis for his nightmares in the years to come . . . Rocky, Horatio and the dreaded soggy penicillin.

It is a mistake to get to an away ground too early. The second match of last season for example. The pavilion was occupied by a nine year old boy who informed us that his name was Hughie. There was also a thirteen and a half stone Irish Wolfhound, who we were told was called Horatio. The pavilion was to be his bridge. He was fastened by a chain with finger-thick links, to an outsize heavy roller. This was embedded in the hay of the outfield and hadn't been moved in living memory.

An enlightening conversation followed.

"You can call me Huge," the diminutive figure explained, "everybody does . . . it's because of my size . . . it's a joke."

We laughed, dutifully.

"Right Huge, are you expecting us? We're the Much Slogging by the Willow cricket team."

"Yes . . . 'they'll' be back in a minute when they've been thrown out of the Ship. If you fill the urn for me I'll get the tea started . . . it's too heavy for me, but if I don't get it going now there won't be any tea until six o'clock."

The urn was filled and then the centre of the field inspected to see if a possible wicket could be found on the non-existent square. A guess was made from the position of the previous week's bowling marks.

Geoff, the skipper, decided that batting would be the lesser of two evils . . . on the assumption that the track wouldn't get any better as the game progressed. (To assume . . . broken down . . . means to make an ass of you and me.)

The hosts arrived, still celebrating their unbeaten record for the season. Two team members pushed the ancient mower to the middle of the field and cut a strip, about a yard wide, that had nothing to do with the previous week's excursion. Two more emerged with a bucket of lime and a brush. A line was marked . . . careful measurements made and another painted . . . a bat and a handle's length in front. The classic twenty two yards were solemnly paced out by the pair . . . independently . . . an average taken and the other creases marked out.

The captain introduced himself:

"Hello, I'm John. I'm afraid we're two short until about four o'clock, which would normally mean that we'd be better off batting first, but the missing pair are our opening batsmen and they've got the only bats and pads, so we'd better field. No need to toss up is there. If you could provide the umpires and keep our scoring book going . . . Oh no . . . we haven't got this season's yet . . . would you mind tearing a page out of yours . . . that would do nicely. Then there's the tea . . . Huge will manage that if your chaps could help him with cutting the bread for the sandwiches . . . he's not too clever with a knife and we have trouble getting him to wash his hands. Tea at half past four if the urn's boiled . . . we haven't marked out the boundary so we can run everything. I think that's all . . . except a couple of your younger lads to sub for us in the outfield."

"But . . ."

"Good, that's agreed then."

The away team dressing room is fully furnished, with two well splintered and splintering wooden benches. The mud and debris from last season's football fixtures has been swept into a corner, directly under the notice from the local council which threatens a ten pound fine if the room isn't cleaned after every game. The total area is equal to that of a small potting shed and there is a strange smell. There are three hooks on the wall, the only window is covered on the outside by a nailed down shutter and light comes from a single forty watt bulb.

The team begins to change, in relays .. more rapidly than usual.

Horatio, in the meantime, who had been flattening the grass like a cow when rain approaches, having seen the visitors safely ensconced in the pavilion, eased himself to his feet.

It was not a graceful movement. The rear end came up first, camel like, almost preceded by the twin spheroid proofs of his retained masculinity, swinging majestically in the breeze. The front legs bent and straightened like a giraffe's.

Standing . . . Horatio was awe inspiring . . . close to two hundred pounds of untrained gundog.

His response to commands was positive and original.

"Fetch" . . . he would lie down.

"Sit" . . . he would lollop away.

"Piss off, you stupid Mutt" . . . he would put his front paws on your shoulders and as you sank to the ground, a yard of tongue would wash your face.

He stood, straining against the chain, until he realised that the immovable object really was . . . and sighed a halitosis sigh.

Enter, upstage right, the home captain's eighteen month old son. Built like a two foot high prop forward, his full nappy slung ranchily at knee level, he advanced, making happy noises.

He was known to all as Rocky. Ducking his head only slightly, he toddled beneath Horatio.

In these days of designer built toys, the stimulus to action is very carefully nurtured.

So it was that Rocky, motivated by the gentle to and fro motion of the dog's danglers, nudged them gently with soft, golden hair covered head.

Horatio's eyes opened wide.

Rocky recalled the many hours his father had already spent inculcating the basic elements of ball control in him.

"Rocky"

"Catch" his brain registered . . . as he reached up with small but powerful hands, and squeezed.

Horatio's head jerked upwards. His eyes bulged . . . crossed . . . watered. A look of total astonishment and pain transfixed his noble head.

Deep within him a noise began . . . primeval and very loud.

The teams and spectator heard a roar which was later to be compared with a Grand Prix being started by a low flying Concord.

Horatio shot forward. Rocky turned his first ever backward somersault and landed face down in a ripe green cowpat . . . the texture and taste of which he found quite acceptable.

The roller leapt out of the ground and . . . chariot-like . . . followed as Horatio fled for the safety of the pavilion. They arrived together, the animal sliding to a halt as the concrete and metal cylinder slammed against the away team's dressing room door, sealing it like a tomb. Horatio lowered his rear cautiously to the ground, threw back his head and howled the first of many long and spine-chilling howls.

Inside, the visitors, in various stages of undress . . froze. The forty watt bulb flickered and went out. Light filtered through the unstuffed cracks in the wall . . . revealing pale faces and whiter than white eyeballs.

Moved, at last, by fear rather than a sense of responsibility, Geoff played a captain's innings and tiptoed across the floor to open the door to the highly refined superloo. Enough light came through the essential hygienic holes in the roof to enable him to see. Motivated by thoughts of escape through the window he was not really suprised to find himself facing a brick wall which had replaced the too frequently broken glass of the window. Moved again, this time by the supernatural noise coming from outside, he slammed the door to avail himself of the facilities . . . discovering in due course that the roll of pure white loo paper, which he had seen on the floor, was in fact a soggy, penicillined mass.

Outside, the situation was becoming critical. The home team realised the humour and could take consolation in the thought of the pints which could be extracted from the story.

"Did we ever tell you about the time we couldn't get the visitors out of their dressing room?"

However, there was, after all, a game of cricket to be played and no one wanted to extend the time given to batting in the early spring evening dusk.

They tried everything . . . cajolling . . . threats . . . brute force . . . bribery, nothing had any effect on Horatio.

Until . . . round the corner of the pavilion lurched a green-slime faced Rocky. Seeing his friend and remembering the exciting trip he'd experienced for his successful catching, he raised his arms and his pace quickened.

Total, absolute panic clutched at Horatio. Gathering himself into a strange rhinoceros shape he suddenly unfolded and went careering off across the field, roller bouncing and clattering behind him. For the first time in a decade the cricket pitch was rolled . . . unfortunately straight across the middle. A two yards wide swathe was also created, right through the middle of the allotments at the far side of the field, as dog and destructor passed out of sight.

Ten minutes later, at a quarter past three, the game commenced.

The first three balls produced appeals for L.B.W., . . . all rejected . . . from a bowler who was bowling leg breaks with a left arm round the wicket action. The ball was pitching well wide of the leg stump and the appeals were not going to be acceptable for three reasons:

1. The ball, delivered from a couple of paces away from the crease, wasn't landing anywhere near an imaginary line drawn down the track.
2. The leg break was working.
3. The ball wasn't going to hit the stumps.

The bowler was getting increasingly irate. After the first rejected appeal he complained noisily. Following the second, he ranted and raved. The third produced real drama. Puce in the face, he jumped up and down shouting . . .

"Which stump . . . which stump?"

Eventually he was calm enough for the umpire to ask what he meant.

"Which stump was it missing?" spluttered the latter-day Larwood.

"All of them," said the umpire . . . "by a lot, and if you query another of my decisions I'll ask your captain to remove you from the field of play."

The captain hid behind the wicket keeper.

"Right," said the bowler. "Right", and he strode back to his bowling mark, a black, heel-carved slash on the tender green weeds.

He turned, ran in to bowl, reached the wicket and stopped . . . turned to the umpire and said, "You'll keep an open mind won't you."

"I'll try," said the umpire, with admirable restraint.

The next ball bowled the opening batsman middle peg.

The bowler smiled . . . the captain hid behind fine leg and we changed umpires. We came a very poor second.

"Liquids bottled, jugged and jarred"

CHAPTER THREE

The Tale of Elvis . . . The Prow Rather Than the Stern

Science rears its very ugly 'head'; the deadly combination of Fred Trueman and Emmanuelle; how the opposition were spiked by a poisonous potion without touching a drop.

Balls have always been controversial.

Differences in quality are not always easy to spot when you're holding a brand-new, made in Bangladesh, masterpiece. It is not until after it has been struck with force that the shape-retention-factor can be assessed. In addition it takes two overs on a wet July outfield, with occasional forays into the nettles, to judge the water-absorbency-rate . . . which also alters the carefully calculated weight.

Cricketers, ever inventive, have devised ways and means of prolonging, extending and revitalising the life cycle of balls.

Letters have been written to the M.C.C.

The obvious advantage to the side bowling first, if there is a new cherry and there's only one ball for the two innings, is that it is easier to work on a new 'pill'.

"Is it true," I hear you asking, " that the great Dennis of Compton, he of shiny headed fame, was only able to produce his famous 'Chinaman' after running his hand over his immaculate hair?"

And what about the controversy over the face cream used by the limp wristed Australian, which combined with sweat . . . or in his case . . . perspiration, seemed to keep the ball in pristine condition for more overs than was credible.

So it was that the elders from the Tin Tabernacle Selectors . . . and guess what they were called for short . . . persuaded Elvis, the long-blond-haired, gangly youth who was the nearest the team had to a fast bowler . . . that he should allow the team to decide on his hair cream on important match days.

This of course, necessitated the formation of a sub-committee and an immediate emergency meeting in the back room of the Fox.

An assortment of liquids, bottled, jugged and jarred was assembled on the table, together with certain unlabelled substances which came from a variety of sources. The pub kitchen, Yvette's bedroom, Ben's and Bill's potting shed and the local chemists . . . to name but four.

Roger had brought along a spare football coupon with the intention of keeping a check on the permutations. This was eventually rolled up to make a funnel, through which a selection of coloured powders and potions were poured into a demi-john, which became the mixing pot. This was easy to cork and shake, so that the resulting cocktails could be poured into glasses and labelled.

Many mixtures were tried and found wanting. A few were thrown away, but as the evening wore on the majority were drunk, in the interest of scientific research, to suitable toasts: viz . . .

"Elvis, you little beaut," a poor attempt at an Oz accent by Nigel. "Never mind your Tequila Sunset, this colourful concoction looks too tasty to waste on transforming a cricket match. Here's mud in your eye."

"Cheers, El, this is too good to waste on your flea ridden thatch."

"Elv, we'll just pass this through the proper channels to see if it stands the test of time."

Stands proved to be appropriate.

The final mixture, which smelt like a careless blend of badly fermented beer and stale urine, had the consistency of slightly lumpy porridge, the shining globules of which attached themselves with artistic regularity to Elvis's long locks. In fairness he didn't look at lot different. The colour a little darker perhaps, but the style more or less the same. He was approved by the senior members of the selection committee and admired by Yvette the barmaid, who gave the impression that she couldn't wait to run her fingers through the congealing contours.

Fortunately it rained that night and the magic potion was washed right out of Elvis's hair.

Match day dawned with unaccustomed splendour and the full glory of the July sun shone down on Geoff as he crossed his fingers and tossed the lucky penny. Unfortunately the opposing captain called correctly . . . fortunately and to everyone's amazement, he elected to bat. The one and only new ball was discovered and unwrapped.

Elvis's normal bowling action combined the graceless mixture of a rampant hippopotamus in full charge with all the control of a headless chicken. By the time he had reached the bowling crease there was a resemblance to Quasimodo, half way down the outside of the cathedral at Notre Dame, arms flailing wildly and mouth open wide.

By way of contrast, his walk back to his bowling mark was modelled on films he'd seen of Fred Trueman. It was unfortunate that he had seen Emmanuelle at about the same time and the two experiences were intertwined. Clutching the ball in his right hand he would stride away, polishing on his gluteus maximus with bold circular strokes. This alternated with a rapid up and down flourish in the groin area.

On this occasion, however, the whole scenario was changed. In his second over Elvis began to treat the ball as he'd been instructed. On his way back to his bowling mark he dutifully ran his left hand through his hair and proceeded to smear the elixir on to one side of the ball. Maintaining a protective, hunch shouldered walk he then ran his hand through his hair again . . . then the ball . . . then the hair . . . then the ball. A subtle change began to take place in the ball as the side being worked on gradually became paler and paler, losing not only its shine but also its colour. Which was transfixing itself . . . changing weary, dirty-blond locks into a startling, red, tonsorial masterpiece.

In addition to the colour, the raw oats part of the secret potion was acting as a setting lotion, so that the hair was beginning to stick out in spikes.

The universal cameraderie of cricketers everywhere asserted itself and nobody mentioned to Elvis that there was anything wrong. The batsmen maintained straight faces and even straighter bats as the fielders began to fall about with ill-concealed mirth, whenever Elvis's back was turned. Eventually the sensors in Elvis's left hand began to pass messages to his brain that changes were taking place on his head.

He left . . . the field . . . the village and the county.

"Nobody mentioned to Elvis"

Dryden knew what he was talking about when he said:

"By viewing nature, nature's handmaiden, art,
Makes mighty things from small beginnings grow:
Thus fishes first to shipping did impart,
Their tail the rudder, and their head the prow."

Elvis's head the prow indeed . . . and mighty things grew from small beginnings.

Punk had to begin somewhere . . . but on a cricket field!

Letters were written to the M.C.C.

"Passing obnoxious wind"

CHAPTER FOUR

Nigel, the Opening Batsman's Tale

Ten of the ways of getting out without incurring the wrath of the Gods at Lords, who normally are the only ones who can re-write the Laws.

Seven thirty on a Saturday evening, the final 'ten' made and the match lost, we embarked on another of our cricketing law re-writes.

"There are ten methods of getting out," said Nigel, "what are they?"

"Never mind those," a disgruntled l.b.w.'d voice replied, "what about the real ten.?"

1. C.N.D. On a dry wicket (there was one in 1983, two in 1976), the batsman can cause undue interference, particularly to the wicket keeper, by shuffling his feet and banging his bat into the hole he has just created, causing an atomic-like cloud to rise.
   CREATING NUCLEAR DUSTSTORM.

2. P.O.W. Not Prisoner of War . . . but a serious assault on the close fielders. Usually occurs at Sunday games, after the batsman has spent Saturday night at the local Indian Restaurant and Tandooried home to put the loo rolls in the fridge.
   PASSING OBNOXIOUS WIND.

3. C.C.C. This applies to the married, multi-blessed fathers. The precise moment happens just when the fast bowler is in mid-run. Out of the corner of his eye the batsman sees a small, instantly recognizable shape appearing on top of the pavilion and is undone.

CHILDREN CREATING CHAOS.

4. U.C. This covers a whole range of minor offences from goosing the tea lady to kicking the umpire's dog . . . or kicking the tea lady and goosing the umpire's dog. The batsman is given out at the first appeal.

UNGENTLEMANLY CONDUCT.

5. S.O. This happens at the beginning of the cricket season in shared pavilions. The football team are occupying the bar celebrating the fact that the season is over. The batsman facing is distracted by an earth shattering cheer. Another bottle of Creme de Menthe has been emptied.

SPOOFED OUT.

"Improperly dressed"

6. I. The big 'I'. Having seen Graham Gooch batting so successfully by adopting an upright posture with bat swinging in the air six inches off the ground, the batsman attempts a similar style and is yorked first ball. Also applies to the Peter Willey look-alikes who are immediately L.B.W.

IMITATION.

7. I.D. At its most extreme this can also prove to be painful. When for example a thigh pad is attached too loosely . . . or carelessly tied . . . it is liable to slip and attempt to disappear up the fundamental orifice.

IMPROPERLY DRESSED.

8. P. Claiming to have torn a Ham String while clutching the wrong part of the leg. The runner . . . reluctant runner . . . is given out even though he is three yards past the wicket keeper. This entails a certain amount of understanding between the fielding side and the umpire.

POSING.

9. O.E.D. Usually tail enders who scent the chance of glory, if they can just bat out the last twenty minutes. They are oblivious to the agitation of the fielding side, as lights go on in the club house and people emerge clutching large glasses of 'Falling over Water'.

OVER ENTHUSIASTIC DEFENCE

10. U.U. For this offence . . . the most serious, the batsman is given out without anyone appealing. Usually perpetrated in all innocence by questioning . . . i.e. asking the umpire for an unusual guard . . . viz . . . .

"Could I have the offside edge of my bat . . . that's that one . . . in line with the near side edge of my legstump . . . that's that one?" Forgetting that the umpire has already batted for the other side and been given out L.B.W.

UPSETTING THE UMPIRE.

Asking the umpire, in the break between overs if he can name the ten reasons for being out, can have the same effect.

"Piers ffrench-Epistle"

CHAPTER FIVE

Roger the Senior Professional's Tale

In which Piers ffrenche-Epistle joins the club and is introduced to 'Strategy' by Lobby Lowslung, the wicket keeper and Winston Garfield Dubois Smith, fast bowler extraordinaire.

Home advantage, selection and use of the new ball; who bats first loses; control of time; strategy.

Roger was leaning against the steel mesh which protected the club bar from unwelcome intruders. He would have to speak to the committee about their ruling that the bar would not open on Sundays when the team was playing away. The sour taste of yesterday's defeat and last night's over indulgence combined to increase his gloom.

"I say . . . are you Woger?"

The lisp was severe. Roger turned and shielded his eyes as his eyes adjusted to the fiery blazing colours of the striped blazer.

"Yes . . . I'm Woger . . . Roger . . . who are you?

"Piers . . . Piers ffrenche-Epistle . . . on vac from Cambwidge . . . I was told you were one short."

"At least . . . what do you do?"

"Philosophy, psychology and anthropology . . . I'm in my final year."

"You deserve to be. No . . . I meant on the cricket field," Roger's gentleness owed a great deal to the fragile state of his head.

"Oh . . . Sowwy . . . Well I'm a weasonable bat . . . plenty of patience . . . I usually open."

"Good. We could do with a stayer to go in first."

Piers is obviously pleased by his acceptance as a man of substance . . . doubts come later.

"Shall I assume that I open then?"

A shadow falls over them as they are joined by Winston, six foot six inches and seventeen stone of fast bowler, West Indian with a cockney accent. The voice is slightly high pitched, a legacy of tight Y fronts and left heel being driven into the ground . . . as any ancient quickie will tell you.

" 'Ere, you don't assume nuffink . . . If Roger says we could do with a stayer then his mate Geoff, who just happens to be the captain, will certainly agree . . . Roger being the senior professional like. Pity abaht the helmet though in'it."

Roger looked up too sharply and shuddered as his head caught up with his eyes.

"What do you know about the helmet, that's supposed to be a committee decision."

"That's as maybe," said Winston, "but we ain't gettin' one and that's for sure."

Piers smiled the smile of innocence.

"It won't weally bother me, I'm used to quick twacks . . . fast and twue that is . . ."

Winston smiled the smile of experience.

"Yeah . . . but today we're playin' at Little Scratchin on the Borrem. Forget fast and true . . . think ploughed field, roughly rolled . . . and a chucker with a double jointed elbow."

Piers was puzzled. "But doesn't he get called?"

"Sure," said Winston, "all sorts of things. But the home umpire always stands at square leg and he doesn't say anything . . . just smiles."

Hovering beside Winston is the lugubrious figure of Lobby Lowslung, the team's wicket keeper. The polished dome of his head is on a level with Winston's armpit. By way of contrast his face is a mass of hair, thick moustache, splendid sideboards and a generous beard. His voice comes from somewhere beneath his boots . . . deep in the earth . . . it would make a bass sound like a boy soprano.

"Where do you play?"

"Actually, I play for the Gnomes." Piers was neither overawed by the voice or conscious of the possible comparison with the hirsute miniature in front of him.

Neither was Lobby.

"Where . . . 'Who for?' . . . Where's your ground?"

"Gnomes," said Piers, "gnomes . . . you know . . . as in 'no home . . . nomadic' . . . we haven't actually got a ground so we play all our fixtures away."

"But that's terrible," Lobby said, "that means you never get a chance to apply 'Strategy'."

Piers looked puzzled.

"Strategy"

"Strategy," said Lobby, "is the word Geoff, our skipper, uses to denote the various almost illegal means of taking full advantage of playing at home."

"Do you mean knowing the twack."

"Well, yes, there's that as well."

"As well as what?"

"Winning the toss for a start," said Lobby.

"But surely that's a fifty-fifty chance." Piers wasn't at university for nothing.

"Yeeees," said Lobby, "but only if the opposing captain gets to see the coin."

"But that's . . ." Piers was indignant.

"Strategy . . . Yes . . . Now you're beginning to understand."

"What happens if the coin is seen and the toss is lost?"

Winston could contain himself no longer.

"That's when you use 'Advanced Strategy'," he said, "Geoff will arrange . . . or rearrange . . . the timings according to whether the opposition decide to bat or field."

Piers shook his head, "I'm afwaid you've lost me again."

Winston was very patient.

"Suppose it's a 2-30 start. If the opposition elect to bat first then you say, 'Tea at four thirty'. If they put you in, then you say, 'Tea at five o'clock'."

"That way, said Lobby, "whatever happens you bat for two and a half hours and only field for a maximum of two hours."

"I'm beginning to understand," said Piers, "stwategy . . . stwategy."

"Then there's the ball," said Winston.

"But you can't do much about that."

"Wrong. Think 'Strategy'. When you go out to toss up you're carrying a used ball . . . good shape but no shine. If they opt to bowl that's the match ball, but if they decide to bat then you say . . . 'One of our sponsors . . .'."

"Note that," interrupted Lobby, "One . . . of our sponsors, nice touch that."

"One of our sponsors," continued Winston, "has kindly provided the ball for today's game . . . and you produce an unwrapped cherry from your pocket."

"Here endeth the first lesson," said Roger, "have you got a car young 'un?"
"Errr . . . yes," said Piers.
"Good, we'll come with you then. The gear can go in your boot."

Winston indicates that the honour of carrying the kit is Piers . . . and winks at him.
"Remember," he said. "Strategy."

"Toby, secretary"

CHAPTER SIX

Toby, the Secretary's Tale

In which we discover how to avoid being elected to office; how to pass the accounts without losing the treasurer; voting rituals; inside the A.G.M.

"I suppose it's time we got started then."

It was a statement rather than a question . . . delivered without too much enthusiasm. Lobby was still smarting from the last A.G.M. when he'd been elected Chairman of the club. It was an honour he could have done without; it was always the Chairman who took the stick whenever anything went wrong. Apart from which it meant that he'd had to control the committee meetings over the past year . . . making sure that everyone . . . but EVERYONE . . . had their say . . . and still ensuring that the meetings closed ten minutes before the bar. It was a position full of stress and calling for a delicacy of touch that Lobby hadn't so far exhibited.

He wouldn't have minded if he'd expressed some enthusiasm for the post . . . or even a willingness to be considered. The truth was that he'd been elected because he happened to be the one who was snoring at that particular moment. When he woke up it was too late . . . he'd been proposed, seconded, a vote taken and those who were grateful for their own escape had given their unanimous consent.

There was a general grumbling of dissent as the assembled members finished their pints and made their way into the back

"Lobby Lowslung, chairman"

room. It was a rule that drinks were not allowed into meetings . . . a rule passed after the night an irate member had turned the tables on a motion he'd objected to . . . literally . . . and the club had lost half of it's stock of glasses.

Toby looked up as they entered. This had been his third year as secretary. In the first two years he'd been so involved . . . and there had been so many contentious issues . . . that he'd despaired of ever being able to hand over. This year, however, would be different. He was determined that he would just resign . . . not put himself forward . . . and hand over the ever growing mountain of paper. He peered myopically from behind his many files and the sheaves of correspondence and sighed. One only needed to look at the disgruntled faces as the room filled up to know that this wasn't going to be an easy meeting.

There were six places set at the top table and they faced the rows of assorted chairs in the body of the small hall . . . across a divide made up of about three yards and several miles of hostility. The back seats filled up first. It wasn't the customary shyness of the great British audience at gatherings . . . rather a dcsire to be nearest the door and first out when the meeting closed . . . in order to win the race to the bar.

The committee took their places. Toby on the extreme right occupied more than his fair share of table space. This was compensated for by Geoff, the captain, who sat down and reach into his inside pocket, produced a small scrap of paper and placed it carefully on the space in front of him. His report wasn't going to take too long. He'd once made the mistake of attempting to recall individual performances and matches. He'd gone on so long that the barman had taken great delight in slamming the bar grill down, calling last orders as he did so. Apart from which Geoff had missed out several players and it was several weeks before the whole team were on speaking terms with him.

Winston lowered himself gently into a chair of indeterminate age and strength. He smiled broadly as it held his sixteen plus stone and prepared to give his support to everybody. He knew that his success as Social Secretary owed a great deal to his expansive smile . . . particularly useful when bearing bad news . . . and his six foot six inch frame. He put his arm round Lobby.

"What we need, my son," he said, "is a nice, quiet, quick meeting. A new committee and back to the bar to pull them to pieces."

The final two places were taken up by Gary, the Fixture Secretary, clutching scraps of paper and last year's diary and Richard the treasurer, who sat very straight and very still, staring sightlessly ahead, a pile of cyclostyled accounts in front of him. The timing of when they would actually be given out was dependant on the mood of the meeting. A friendly reception might mean that the members received a copy before Richard summarised them . . . any hostility and they'd be lucky to get them at closing time . . . if at all.

Lobby banged on the table with his fist, causing chaos but gaining attention.

"First item . . . minutes of the last meeting . . . is it your wish that I should take these as read?"

"What about matters arising? "the query came from the back of the hall.

"What about them?" Winston stood up.

"I just wondered if . . ."

"No matters arising," Lobby smiled for the first time for months.

"Next item."

He continued to smile . . . this was the moment when they were all going to get off the hook. They'd decided at a private meeting in the Fox that lunchtime that they would all resign and not put themselves up for re-election.

"The next item on the agenda is the election of officials to run the club for the next year." He took a deep breath. It was a mistake.

"I propose," a disembodied voice came from the back, "I propose that we elect the whole committee 'en bloc', on the grounds that it's just possible that we could do worse."

"Seconded," several enthusiastic voices tried to gain a place in the minutes.

"All those in favour," it was the first speaker again.

There was a universal lowing of assent and a mass exodus from the room before the committee . . . past and present . . . realised that they'd encountered a classic pre-empting.

"Albert"

CHAPTER SEVEN

Albert, the President's Tale

Reflections on the previous year's tour; the importance of the playing mix between the youngsters and the 'Crumblies'; beautiful sheep and randy terriers.

It is the night of the annual dinner for those players who toured last season. Well dined and extremely well wined, thirty assorted players are waiting for the report that is due to be given by the president, Albert. A sprightly, little grey haired pensioner, in his early seventies he rises to his feet to the customary cries of;

"Stand up, Albert."

"Snow on the roof but plenty of fire below."

"Get your finger up, Albert. If Winston appeals it must be out."

"Before I begin," Albert began, "there's a story I heard about Roger. He was clearing a house and had loaded furniture from it for sale. He took it round to the local dealer and asked the bossman to come and look at the goods.

"What've you got then?"

"Well, there's a piano."

"What sort?"

"It's a Steinway."

"Nah . . . we've got plenty of those." He turns and shouts through the warehouse door.

"Cedric."

"Yeah."

"How many Steinways we got?"

"Dozens."

"I'll give you ten pounds."

"What else you got Roger?"

"Well, I've got a violin."

"What sort?"

"It's a Stradivarius."

"Cedric."

"Yeah."

"How many Stradivarius's we got?"

" 'Undreds."

"Five pounds."

"What else you got?"

Roger climbs into his van and struggles back clutching to his stomach a wooden ball the size of a football.

"What's that?"

"This is one of the testicles from the Wooden Horse of Troy . . . and before you shout through to Cedric . . . the other one's in the van."

It was a little while before Albert was allowed to continue.

"Which brings us," he said, "to the tour . . . another load of old bollocks. How is it possible for one of the finest sides in the country . . . county . . . well this side of the river . . . to arrange five games in a week and not win one of them? Leaving aside the two players who fell in love with the sheep and weren't able to concentrate, and the fact that Piers discovered that Grosch was alcoholic."

"It wasn't difficult to lose," a voice interrupted from the far end of the table.

"The nearest you got to winning," said the President, "was in the first fixture at Upham Creek. You'd actually got into double figures without losing a wicket when the rains came. We thought the opposition was impressed as well, the way the whole of their side rushed out to put the covers on the wicket . . . it was a pity that they put them on their track for Saturday and trampled all over the pitch we were playing on."

There was a brief pause as young Piers ffrenche-Epistle, looking a whiter shade than the club's pads had ever been, left the room.

"Unfortunately," continued Albert, "the early finish to the game meant that tea was taken very early . . . after we'd met the Fox Terrier which was rushing around trying to get it's leg over everything in sight.

It was a pity that we expressed our curiosity about him . . . and received the explanation from their skipper . . . I blame our defeats on the rest of the tour on that dog. For those of you who weren't within earshot . . . the explanation of his behaviour was that they fed him on fairy cakes and he got a real stomper on. The names of

"The Fox Terrier"

our team who ate more than three fairy cakes do not need to be mentioned here as they are the ones who performed at the night club on the Monday and not on the field for the rest of the week."

"Stop blaming the youngsters," an indignant voice interrupted.

"I'm not talking about the players," said Albert with a smile.

"I was referring to the elder members of the party, those geriatric gentlemen you refer to so aptly as 'The Crumblies'."

"Difficult not to recognise the class shots"

CHAPTER EIGHT

Gary, the Fixture Secretary's Tale

The game against a College from the University, incorporating the boat race; the schooner race and the metre of ale. Games that students play.

Gary sat at his desk, facing his class of thirty five fourth year juniors. They were very understanding. They knew that on Monday morning it was advisable to keep a low profile while 'Sir' recovered from the week end's cricket.

'It wasn't anybody's fault,' thought Gary, as he rested his head in his cupped hands with the care he would have given a thin shelled egg. When he'd arranged the fixture with Upham College from Bullford University it was in the expectation that there would be a touch of class about both the cricket and their opponents.

Bloody Piers . . . what a little pillock he'd turned out to be . . . didn't know which side his bread was buttered. The fact that he'd got his maiden ton for the club only indicated that there was truth in the rumours that Public School was the way to get on in life . . . whether you were playing cricket or becoming a Member of Parliament. And there's a liar in Parliament . . . you've only got to look at the word . . . there it is in the middle. Their fixture secretary was a liar alright.

'We're at half stwength, weally and twuly . . . it's the exam season'

Did they all talk like Piers? Or was it just the cricketers?

It was the first time Gary had ever seen Geoff, the captain, out-manoeuvered. All the customary strategy went by the board as the University skipper had the audacity to toss up with his own coin . . . Yes it was their home game but that hadn't mattered before . . . toss up and announce the result as the coin went back into his pocket. Then produce that tatty old ball and say they'd bat. Talk about hoist by his own petard. Just when they'd been about to enjoy the hospitality of the beer tent . . . a canvas castle full of pint plastic pots and assorted barrels. Never mind they'd thought, if the college were really as weak as they said, then they could all be quaffing ale by teatime.

They'd started well, taken a couple of early wickets and had the college struggling at 7 for 2. It looked good on the elaborate scoreboard. Then they became aware of a sudden celebration in the marquee . . . but the reason wasn't apparent until later. Sooner, actually, but they hadn't read the fairly obvious clues. They knew the University game against Yorkshire had finished early the previous day, but they didn't immediately recognise the number five, six and seven batsmen as they came to the crease during the course of the afternoon. However it was difficult not to recognise the class as shots were played that they'd only previously seen on television.

"Yes, Kevin." Gary forced himself to deal with the small boy standing at the side of his desk. "I realise you've been reading for half an hour. What you do now is take these sheets of paper, give them out to the class and you can all spend the time up to lunch time writing about what you've read."

Winston had enjoyed his first spell. Taking three wickets and then patrolling the long leg boundary while the spinners struggled. Then he'd been brought back for a second spell and subjected to the most awful indignities. Nobody could remember anyone ever straight driving Winston for six . . . let alone repeating the insult. Then when he'd become really annoyed and tried digging the ball in short to intimidate the young pretenders they'd dropped their shoulder in classic style and hooked him for three further sixes. It had been too much. Winston had limped off the field and gone straight for the barrel of 'Wobin Hood's Weal Ale' where he'd spent the rest of the afternoon.

The score at the interval made interesting reading for statisticians. Thanks to the fairly prompt start just after two o'clock, . . . and the reversed strategy of the opposition in fixing tea for four forty five . . . the opposition had enjoyed two and three quarter hours batting. During that time the village had bowled a creditable forty-five overs and the scoring rate had been kept down to below the ten an over it threatened to be at one stage. This meant . . .

Gary groaned as he remembered and the class looked up expectantly.

"Settle down, you've fifteen minutes to go before you sample the delights of Monday's meal . . . which will be B.B.C. as you all know . . . which stands for?"

"Bangers, beans and chips." The reply was enthusiastic.

Gary's thoughts went back to Sunday . . . a mere 417 for 7. This was a record beyond comprehension and would make an interesting headline in the local paper if it wasn't suppressed. Four hundred and seventeen . . . this included three centuries . . . the significance of which became evident after the game.

Tea had been fluid . . . with one side celebrating and the other quite literally drowning their sorrows.

Then the village batted. Of the opening pair . . . Piers ffrenche-Epistle seemed to be completely at home from the word 'Go'. He raised his bat majestically and let the first two balls pass through like rockets to the wicket keeper. The third ball he leant into and stroked through the covers.

"Come," he called, and proceeded to run three.

At the other end Nigel had smiled as the first two balls were delivered. 'This was going to be easy.'

The euphoria induced by four pints of Wobin for tea was, unbeknown to Nigel, scrambling the messages that his brain was passing to his legs. While Piers was running three . . . Nigel fell over twice . . . didn't reach the other end . . . was run out and carried off to a nearby copse of trees to sleep it off.

As it happened the village made the highest score it had ever recorded. Gary altered the possible newspaper headline from . . . "LOCAL SIDE LOSE BY 254" to a more acceptable . . . "LOCAL SIDE SCORE A RECORD 163." Pier's century meant that the ritual reserved for the "Hundred Club' after the game would be enacted four times. Gary remembered only two of these.

Neither side had changed when the racing started. First the 'boatrace' appropriate since the University had won the previous April. This version involved the two sides lining up facing each other across the pitch they'd just played on . . . each player with a pint of 'Wobin's' in front of him. The whistle start saw the opening rower lift his pint, drink it and place the empty pot upside down on top of his head. As soon as this was done the second member of the crew picked up his pint. The village won . . . through a judicious sacrifice of some of the beer over heads and shoulders. Which was a mistake because the University's objection was upheld and a re-run upheld. This became the best of three which Geoff had the good sense to lose.

The 'gallon' race which followed was a far more sedate affair. The sides sat in a circle, alternating places occupied by the opposition. A plastic bucket was half filled with a conservative gallon and duly passed round. Each player lifted the bucket and drank before passing it on. As the level fell so the decision had to be taken when to empty the container . . . success meant glory . . . and the opposition paying. Gary closed his eyes as he remembered how he'd misjudged the contents and his capacity. He'd also missed the Yard of Ale, won by Winston in a happy 9.3 seconds.

The final event as far as he had been concerned was the celebration of the hundreds. The 'ton jug' was produced and filled. Unlike the more common aluminium containers used in clubhouses and pubs throughout the cricket season this was a masterpiece. It was reputed . . . so legend has it . . . to have been used by Napoleon the First, during his 'Hundred Days' as Emperor for the second time in 1815 . . . hence the 'ton jug'. It was a magnificent, two handled, beautifully painted China Chamber Pot. Which was filled . . . and emptied . . . four times.

"The ton jug"

Gary remembered only two. He moaned, five minutes to lunch time . . . the class should learn a little strategy.

"Stand up, class seven. Hands together and eyes closed." As the children stood, heads bowed, waiting for Gary to start singing Grace, he tiptoed noiselessly from the room, leaving the door open behind him.

"Nathaniel and sheep"

CHAPTER NINE

Nathaniel, the Groundsman's Tale

Where sheep may safely graze; red marl, green grass and blue wood; local, national and international sponsorship; the art and angle of pitch marking.

"I'm more than just a groundsman," Nathaniel said to Geoff the club captain, as they stood surveying the cricket square, "I'm an inventor . . . and innovator . . . and entrepreneur."

"You want to be careful," said Geoff, "using language like that . . . someone might ask you what an entrepreneur does."

"I'd tell them," said Nathaniel, "in fact I could give them lots of examples. What about the sheep?"

Geoff shuddered. Where other people used them as a means of drifting gently into sleep, as the woolly bundles jumped gently over stiles; members of the committee were subject to waking nightmares whenever a 'Baaaa' was heard.

"I could never understand why they were banned. They were only here for the day," Nathaniel was indignant, unaware of the depth of feeling his bargain with the shepherd had caused.

Geoff recalled the scene that fateful Friday morning as he'd driven to work. He'd glanced towards the cricket ground as he'd passed and thought for a moment that there had been localised snow overnight. The field was a mass of white, which even as he watched . . . moved.

"The grass," continued Nathaniel, "the grass has never been so well cut . . . cropped in fact . . . I didn't need to use the big mowers for a week afterwards. Then there was the manuring, that was an extra bonus."

Geoff's eyes closed as he remembered. First a holiday in the Gower where he'd seen an item on the breakfast menu which had intrigued him. Laver bread. He'd ordered it thinking it would be similar to the volcanic loaves that he'd enjoyed so much when he'd been in Malta. That was a mistake . . . the dollop of green splodge on his plate had been bad enough. Then, later in the day, he and his wife had been walking across the cliffs to the Mumbles when they'd seen similar blobs on and just off the path. It was a little while before he discovered that the origin of the former was seaweed and the latter was sheep.

On the Saturday morning when the players had arrived at the ground . . . word having travelled . . . the field looked as though a regiment of well trained, badly fed dogs had been lined up in ranks all over the ground . . . including the square . . . and had obeyed whatever the command is that precipitates the performance of canine bodily functions.

They'd lost a fixture over that. The opposition were subjected to Geoff's strategy and found themselves fielding first. They'd commented on the succulent state of the outfield and how green it was. It wasn't until they'd started slipping that they realised that the colour owed more to the fact that the new manure had been spread rather than gathered or dug in.

Kerry Packer must have seen the game, where else would he have got the idea for his multi-coloured cricketing gear?

"Then there was the meat," said Nathaniel. "Every one of the committee members had a joint of lamb. The shepherd showed his gratitude in a way that wouldn't bother the tax man. I think we should have him and his flock back again."

"I'll raise it at the next meeting," said Geoff, as he counted up the various bonuses. "Perhaps they'll agree to October and March." He smiled as he thought of the football club which used the land adjacent to the cricket field.

Nathaniel was also smiling. He had the season well planned. There were so many things he'd seen on television which he could use to the advantage of the club. American Football for example. They painted huge pictures on the playing surface to show which teams were playing. If he used the blue woad he'd discovered, that, together with the red marl he was going to use to bind the wicket together . . . and the white lime to mark out the pitch. Red, white and blue . . . and that was without the green green grass of home. He'd start off with something easy like the Union Jack and then get to his real love . . . advertising. Ever since he'd read about the huge sums that sportsmen were able to get through marketing their 'space', he'd dreamed of the schemes he could use.

Two inch lettering on his overalls would be kept for village shops.

GET YOUR MEAT FROM BERT THE BUTCHER 37, THE HIGH STREET.

"His ancient tractor"

The sides of his ancient tractor and mowing machine could carry district wide happenings . . . since the local press would be interested.

DISPLAY OF AGRICULTURAL EQUIPMENT AT THE MANOR HOUSE.

Then . . . for television . . . the fronts and backs of sightscreens and the roof of the Tin Tabernacle.

MACDONWALDS THE PIZZA QUEEN.

He bowed back as the local bank manager saluted him, paying tribute to the man who had put the village and the bank, on the map. Which would be his next masterpiece, painted on the cricket square.

He knew in his heart of hearts that his real claim to fame would be the angled wicket. Nobody would know it had happened by chance. If he hadn't read about special tracks being prepared for different types of bowlers he'd never have managed to turn what could have been a disaster to such good effect.

It had been a beautiful Sunday. The wicket was perfect and he'd gone out just after he'd had his early, liquid lunch to put the final touch to the wicket for the day . . . marking out. Using his perfectly angled quadrilateral of wood he'd painted the lines at each end with great care.

The fixture was important. Against a side who had beaten the village for the past five seasons. Ever since they'd discovered . . . found . . . bribed . . . a leg spinner to move to their village. A man who could turn the ball on the easiest wicket, and who was doubly blessed with the most extreme case of cross-eyed vision anyone could remember seeing. It totally confused even those of the village players who could recognise and play against leg breaks. As Nigel commented . . . "How can you get the line of the ball when you're watching one eye which is looking at the square leg umpire and another glaring at cover point?"

The trouble . . . or merit of the track on that particular Sunday . . . which Nathaniel kept quiet about afterwards . . . was that the two ends, while being immaculately marked out, were not parallel. Standing square at one end the stumps at the other end appeared to be a good yard too far to the right . . . and viceversa . . . totally confused the legspinner . . . and established Nathaniel's reputation as an expert who could be the answer to English Cricket . . . Thatcherism . . . World Peace.

"His appeal rent the heavens"

CHAPTER TEN

Winston, the Social Secretary's Tale

A personal review of the season and the players by the only team member who is allowed to say anything about anyone . . . a privilege not unrelated to the fact that he weighs in at slightly over seventeen stone and stands six inches above six feet in height.

On the first Saturday in October the back room of the Fox is taken over for the players dinner. It is an occasion at which the unofficial awards are made . . . a task dealt with by Winston, who has been writing a series of fines down throughout the season in a small red book. The meal and copious quantities of beer, lager and wine consumed, he rises to his feet.

"The first and most important presentation to be made tonight is to the player who produced the most outstanding performance of the season. This goes to Lobby Lowslung."

Lobby rises to acknowledge the applause. The difference between his stature seated or standing is minimal. He is a cigar-smoking, ex-army captain. A bachelor with an enormous moustache and sideboards . . . a hirsuteness that compensates for the fact that he is completely and magnificently bald. As a wicketkeeper he is unique. He stands . . . unable to crouch . . . flapping his gloves together like a seal applauding. The long string of bruises down his chest bear testimony to his inefficiency. He stands up to everything and keeps from memory. He has been known to appeal for a stumping having missed all three stumps and the ball. Once down, on a quarter bend of the knees, he is difficult to move.

"On the occasion in question," continued Winston, "Lobby was faced with the exciting prospect of running out one of the opposition . . . or even both . . . when the opening batsmen called . . . 'No . . . Yes . . . No.' One of them was deaf and ran regardless. The throw in was the one of the season which was straight and thudded into Lobby's gloves just at the moment when he was on the clap part of his flapping. With a delicacy of touch worthy of an eccentric, frail old lady wielding a feather duster, Lobby swept round and flattened all three stumps, breaking two. His appeal rent the heavens. He looked up, smiling, to see two batsmen with their bats grounded in his crease."

Tumultuous applause interrupted the proceedings, interspersed with cries of 'Quite right and proper too?' and 'Run up will you!' two of Lobby's favourite shouts . . . the equivalent to cricket of the man who first cried 'Tally Ho!'.

Winston was allowed to continue. "The cricketing brains of the team overflowed with advice. 'Other end. Throw it to the bowler. Get rid of it. Let it go.' Not to be easily deprived of his moment of glory, Lobby, accompanied by both batsmen, raced to the other end, where, with a swallow dive worthy of an Olympic swimming champion, he flattened all three stumps. Everyone appealed, except Lobby who was breathless. The debate as to which of the two batsmen was out is still continuing. Suffice to say that if justice had been done they would both have been out and Lobby Lowslung would have been in the record books for ever."

"Probably," Geoff's voice came from almost under the table, "probably, like the sparrow at Lords, stuffed and mounted."

"Given time," said Winston, "that could probably be arranged. However, the award the 'jug committee' have decided should be given to Lobby is . . . a swimming cap."

Thirty pairs of eyes focused, or tried to focus, on Lobby's bald pate.

Winston held up an ancient pair of wire frame glasses.

"The next award is a collective one. Not, as you may imagine from the nature of the trophy, to the umpires. This goes to the Ground Committee for their truly magnificent effort in designing and building the two sight screens. Twelve feet wide and eight feet high. It is not their fault that due to the slope in the ground at the railway end the batsmen can only see the top eighteen inches. At least they have a clear view of the opposing bowlers feet as he approaches."

Mumblings of dissent from the red faced architects are lost in the general sounds of approbation.

Winston held up his hand for silence. "There is a tradition amongst village sides that the 'elder statesman', usually over fifty, shall be granted the position of first slip. We are lucky in that, when both Ben and Bill are playing, we are blessed with two slips, whatever the state of the match or however slow the bowler. Their combined ages add up to considerably more than a century. They field, not like young Botham, with their forearms on their thighs, but with their gnarled hands on their knees, half crouched, reflective, in toilet training position. The merits of which can be spoken for by those unfortunate to field close to them as they break wind, an occurrance which seems to coincide with the breaking of the crease in their trousers. To our esteemed elders we award a ball each . . . not placed on plinths but in a bag, to be displayed with one slightly higher than the other."

A cry of 'What a load of bollocks' was quickly suppressed.

To Winston's suprise Geoff stood up and asked to be allowed to address that gathering before the brandy began to take effect. Permission granted he produced three objects which he placed on the table in front of him.

"This year we have formed an underground committee to observe, discuss and comment on the behaviour of the Social Secretary."

Winston smiled.

"As a result," Geoff continued, "there are three items which we have decided to award . . . for his comfort, and the well-being of the rest of the team. The first was obtained following the long hot summer in June, when the wickets dried out. Do you remember Winston walking to the middle of the unwatered strip and stamping his foot? Cracks spread to all corners of the square. To avoid a repetition of this we have bought him something which we would like him to wear for all home games, when he is tempted to look at the track before a game."

Geoff gave Winston a small parcel which he solemnly unwrapped to reveal an ancient pair of carpet slippers.

"Secondly, a pair of rubber faced batting gloves. Those of you who were at the rain affected Monday of Cricket Week will remember Winston going out to bat. Having seen the England team swinging their bats as they walked to the wicket, in arcs to loosen their shoulders, he decided that this was his week to be a 'poseur'. It wasn't really his fault that the bat slipped on the second full circle and left his hand to describe a thirty foot arc. We also blame the umpire who was taken to hospital for not watching the incoming batsman."

"The final award is given in an attempt to repeat Winston's greatest thrill of the season. It was, you will recall, the occasion when the bar closed early, the day was hot, a certain number of drinks were bought to last the more intolerant members of the team through the afternoon. Someone in their wisdom decided to get a handful of ice to cool the roughness of the PuertoRican Rum. The

"Look of pleasure on his face"

receptacle for the cubes was selected by pure chance . . . although the size of Winston's plastic box had something to do with it. When the time came for our esteemed number eleven to fit himself for the fray he took his box in complete innocence. The resulting look of pleasure on his face was such that we decided to buy him a cool box to keep his protector in, to cover the possibility of a heat wave next year."

Winston stood up, glowing with pleasure and the feel of the newly inserted plastic pleasure plaything which had been in the coolbag.

"Finally friends," he began, "I would ask you to rise and drink to an absent fiend . . . you heard right, fiend not friend . . . who caused us to suffer our worst humiliation ever. Now, happily no longer with us. I refer of course to Horatio, who cocked his leg over an open electric point and fried his magnificent gonads. Raise your glasses gentlemen, to our only worthy opponent of the season . . . and the electrician who left the plug uncovered."

The last toast of the night duly consumed, the players dispersed to wait for the deceitful April sun.

To be published:

FURTHER TALES FROM THE TIN TABERNACLE